Black Girl Boss

Coloring Story Book

"A Doll Like Me" Story By: Kimberly Gordon
Illustrated By: Jasmine Mills

5D Media Publishing
35 W 31st Street, 6th Floor
New York, NY 10001
www.5Dmedia.org

Ordering Information:
Quantity sales. Special discounts are available on quantity purchases by corporations, associations, and others. For details, contact the publisher at the address above.

Orders by U.S. trade bookstores and wholesalers. Please contact Big Distribution: Tel: (212) 537-7177; Fax: (800) 778-4872 or visit www.5DMedia.org.

Printed in the United States of America

Black Girl Boss / Kimberly Gordon

ISBN-10: 0-9989217-2-6
ISBN-13:978-0-9989217-2-3

First Edition

To My Mini Bosses in Training,
Kylie and Kourtney Rose

"Good Morning Mommy!
I'm ready when you are!"

Mia had prepared all week to have Emily and Abby come over to play.

There was just one more thing left to do before they arrived.

1

"We can go to the Toy Store after I am done working for the day," Mom said.

Mia was happy to hear this. She knew it would not be long before they left. Her Mom worked on making clothes for her Fashion Design business every day, but only worked for a few hours on Saturdays.

"I want to buy a doll just like me, and one like my little sister Rosie too?" Mia said.

Mia enjoyed helping her parents on
the weekends. It made her feel almost like
a grown up.

Mia dreamed of having a business and a bank account too, just like Mom. But, now she only had a piggy bank with a few coins in it.

Mia loved the many bright colors of the different rolls of cloth Mom had arranged around the home office, and how they smelled. Sometimes she played with them and ran her fingers over the cloth or placed them against her cheek. They felt nice and smooth.

"Can my doll be just like me, and wear a dress like mine?" Mia asked Mom as the business phone started to ring. "Hello, KJ Fashion Designs, how may I help you?" Mia said to the caller.

Mia was only eight years old, but knew how to answer the phone and how to talk to customers just like Mom.

When Mom called here workers together into her office for a meeting, Mia went into the kitchen and grabbed some snacks.

"Mia, you can stay and listen if you want," Mom said.

Mia smiled and quickly sat down in the
chair facing the office window. That way
she could look outside if she got bored.
There were no toys in Moms workplace.

"I wish I had my doll already,"
Mia thought.

Mia heard them talk about
customers, sales, advertisements,
fashion trends and other things.
Some of the words she understood,
others she did not.

Then Mom spoke about coming up with
"something new" to sell at the Big Town Fair,
which made Mia began thinking too.
"What about making something for children?"
Mia suggested.

Mia had waited patiently all morning After the meeting Mom drive them to go the Toy Store to buy her doll.

When they arrived Mia dashed straight to the doll section. "I want a doll that plays a guitar and wears a purple superhero cape," Mia said.

"I don't think you'll find that at all here," Mom replied.

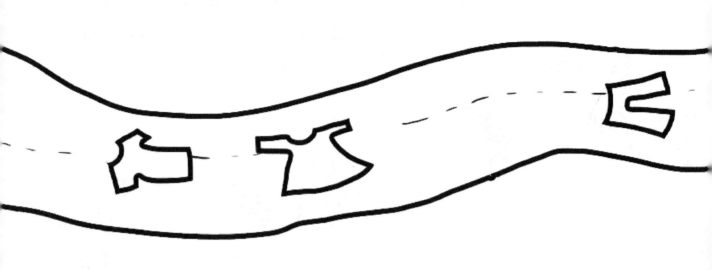

"Then I'll look for one with chocolate color skin and curly hair, just like me."

There were rows and rows of dolls.
But none of the dolls would do.

At the next store they went to the super hero aisle. "But none of the superheroes are little girls," said Mia.

And the next store had an entire section of musician dolls, but not one had curly hair.

Mia and her mom checked many other stores but found no doll just like Mia, and soon it was time for Emily and Abby to come over to play.

"But I'm a chocolate ballerina, that plays guitar," Mia said has they headed home. "Why can't I find a doll that is?"

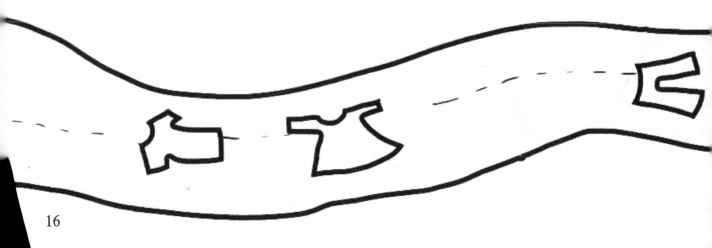

"We can look at more stores tomorrow sweet heart. Maybe if we find different doll outfits, we can dress a doll that looks a little like you," Mom suggested on their way home.

That gave Mia an idea. "Mommy, we can't find a doll like me, but you can make one for me," she said.

"Okay, Mia," Mom said. "I will design dolls just for you and your friends. I will cut out the pieces, and you can build them all by yourself!"

"I want a princess doll that plays soccer," said Emily.

"I want my doll to be a fairy that wears blue jeans," said Abby.

"Can my doll be a chocolate ballerina, like me?" Rosie asked Mom.

"Select the fabric for the outfits," Mom said.

"Then I will cut out the dolls and their outfits, then you can each make one just like you."

The girls cut, stitched and pasted all day. Mom showed them how and Grandma pitched in and helped too. In the end, they had four beautiful dolls.

"Abracadabra" said Abby as her doll tossed pretend fairy dust into the air, while Emily shouted "goal" as her doll kicked imaginary soccer balls.

Mia whipped her dolls cape from side to side, as Rosie twirled around the living room.

"Daddy, I think we should take our dolls to show and tell on Monday," Mia said.

She had planned on bringing fabric samples form Moms office, but her doll was much more fun.

"That's a very good idea, Mia," Dad responded.

At school on Monday, Mia, Emily and Abby brought in their dolls in for show and tell.

Many parents were there. Mom even brought Rosie. When it was Mia's turn, she felt a little nervous, but she held up her doll and spoke.

"My mom is a fashion designer," she told the class. "This weekend we worked together to make these dolls. They are very special because we built them all by ourselves."

Then Emily, Abby and Rosie joined Mia and
held up their dolls for all to see.

Many of the other parents wanted to know how they could get one of the dolls for their daughters. "I think you have discovered our 'something new' Mia," Mom said with a smile.

Mia and Mom worked for weeks preparing for the Big Town Fair.

Mom spent hours cutting doll pieces and designing mini doll outfits, while Mia helped pull everything into Doll Design Kits, so other children could easily build a doll like them. Many of the other parents wanted to know how they could get one of the dolls for their daughters.

"I think you have discovered our 'something new' Mia," Mom said with a smile.

They also created display dolls of all shapes and shades.

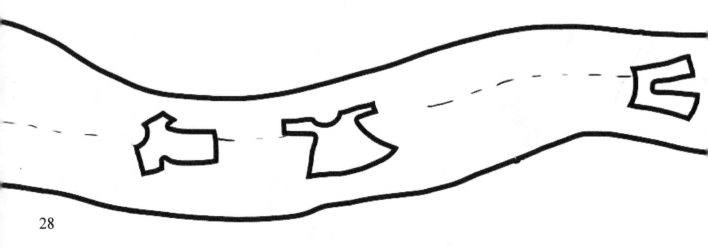

At the Big Town Fair, parents were glad to see dolls they had never seen before. And their children were excited that they could make their own doll at home just as Mia did.
Many purchased a Doll Design Kit to take home.
"Look Mommy, they are buying our Doll Kits!" Mia said.

"I'm so glad and I have you to thank for this. We should call them Mia Dolls, after you."

"Can my doll be a business owner too?" Mia asked. "Of course she can," Mom replied with a smile.

THE END